Titles in More First Flight

Badger Publishing Limited
Oldmedow Road, Hardwick Industrial Estate,
King's Lynn PE30 4JJ
Telephone: 01438 791037
www.badgerlearning.co.uk

2 4 6 8 10 9 7 5 3 1

Into The Deep ISBN 978-1-84926-448-8
First edition © 2012
This second edition © 2016

Text © Jonny Zucker 2011
Complete work © Badger Publishing Limited 2011

Badger Publishing would like to thank Jonny Zucker for his help
in putting this series together.

Publisher: David Jamieson
Senior Editor: Danny Pearson
Design: Fiona Grant
Illustration: David Shephard

INTO THE DEEP

CONTENTS

Badger LEARNING

New words:

accident   tunnel

drilling   emerging

crouched   freedom

Main characters:

Carl

Keesha

4

CHAPTER 1
Accident

Keesha and Carl's Dad worked in a mine.

The work was hard, dirty and tiring, but he did not complain.

"My Dad was a miner and his Dad was a miner," he told Keesha and Carl. "It is what I know."

One Monday morning, Keesha and Carl were in school when they were called out of class.

They were told to go to the school office.

Their Mum was there waiting for them.
She looked as if she had been crying.

"What is the matter?" asked Keesha.

"There has been an accident at the mine," she told them.

"NO!" cried Carl.

"Your Dad is trapped down there with twenty other men."

"Are they alive?" asked Keesha.

"Yes," nodded their Mum. "They have a phone that works down there."

"Will they be able to get out?" asked Carl.

"It doesn't look good," said their Mum. "In fact, it looks very bad."

CHAPTER 2
Trust Us

The three of them drove to the mine.

Lots of the miners' wives and children were already there.

A man from the company, called Mr Trent, came to talk to them. "I am sorry this has happened," he said.

"What are you doing to get them out?" asked Keesha.

"We are still talking about what to do," he replied. "Drilling down to reach them, could be very dangerous."

"But you have to do something!" shouted Carl.

"Of course we will," said Mr Trent. "Please trust us."

None of the families wanted to leave
the site. So tents were put up for them.

"We will stay here until your father gets
out safely," said their Mum.

By the time it got dark, there was still no drilling.

"Why aren't they doing anything yet?" asked Keesha angrily.

"I know it is hard," said their Mum, "but we will just have to wait."

CHAPTER 3
Library

The next day, Carl and Keesha's Mum gave them a lift into the town.

She went to buy some food.

They went to the library.

They found lots of books about the local area and the mine.

"Hey, look at this!" said Keesha, holding up a very old book. "It says that an escape tunnel was dug when the mine was first opened."

"But that was over a hundred years ago," replied Carl, looking at the map in the book.

But they didn't have much time to look because their Mum appeared.

"Don't tell her about this," whispered Keesha.

Back at the site there was still no drilling. Keesha and Carl hurried to find Mr Trent.

They told him about the old escape tunnel.

"Where is it?" he asked.

They took him to the place they'd seen on the map.

They scraped at the ground but there was no tunnel.

"But it was there in the book!" said Keesha.

"You have wasted my time!" snapped Mr Trent.

"We're sorry, but..." said Carl.

"No buts," said Mr Trent. "Leave the rescue to us and stay out of it!"

CHAPTER 4
Tunnel

After supper, something suddenly hit Keesha.

"We were looking at that map upside down!" she cried.

"So the tunnel is not where we thought it was?" asked Carl.

"No," said Keesha. "It is over there."

They hurried to the new spot.

They crouched down and began moving
mud and stones. But someone stood in
their way.

It was Mr Trent.

"I told you to leave things to us!"
he said angrily.

Keesha and Carl stood up and started
walking back to their tent.

But when they saw Mr Trent had gone,
they ran back to the spot.

They worked fast, moving the mud and stones.

Fifteen minutes later, they found a panel.

Keesha yanked it open and they found themselves looking into a dark tunnel.

It was pitch black inside the tunnel and there wasn't much room to move.

But after twisting and turning they started moving forwards. It was slow going but finally they saw some light up ahead.

There was another panel.

At first it would not move, but Keesha and Carl worked together and moved it aside.

But then they saw something else.

It was a huge slab of stone. And it was blocking their way.

"Oh no!" cried Carl.

But Keesha started kicking at the rock.

Carl joined her and suddenly the rock fell away.

Below them, stood twenty miners, including their Dad. The lamps on their helmets lit up the space.

"CARL! KEESHA!" cried their Dad,
running towards them.

Chapter 5
Heroes

Carl and Keesha told their Dad and the other miners about how they'd found the escape tunnel.

"It's been blocked for years," said Keesha.

"You are BRILLIANT!" shouted their Dad.

Up above ground, Mr Trent was talking to all the TV cameras and newspaper people. "We will begin drilling tomorrow," he said. "We should get the men out by the end of the month."

At that moment, Keesha and Carl appeared, with all twenty miners behind them.

There were screams all round the site as the miners' families rushed towards them.

Mr Trent nearly got trampled under people's feet.

All of the cameras and reporters turned to face the miners.

"It's the twenty heroes!" someone shouted.

"These two are the true heroes!" cried their Dad. "Without them, we would have been down there for a very long time."

There were massive cheers and clapping for Keesha and Carl.

When all of the excitement died down, Mr Trent said he wanted to put a big company sign at the top of the tunnel, telling people what happened, but the miners said no.

Six weeks later a large statue was unveiled, showing Keesha, Carl and the twenty miners, emerging from the tunnel to freedom.

MINERS

- In 2010, 33 miners in Chile were trapped half a mile underground.

- They were very lucky because when the rock collapsed, they were in the lunch space, which was safe.

- No one on the surface knew they were alive for 17 days.

- In those first 17 days, the miners lived on two mouthfuls of tuna fish and a sip of milk, every 48 hours.

- When the miners were finally lifted to safety, they had been underground for 69 days.

- *They were taken to the surface in a special steel cage named 'Phoenix.'*

- *They had to wear sunglasses at first because they hadn't seen natural light for over two months.*

- *'Los 33' were not the first Chilean miners to get trapped underground.*

- *Every year, thousands of miners around the world get trapped down in mines. Not all are so lucky.*

31

QUESTIONS

- What did the families of the trapped miners do when they got to the mine?

- What did Mr Trent say about the rescue plan?

- Where did Keesha and Carl go to read up about the history of the mine?

- Why didn't they tell their Mum about their plan?

- What stood in their way at the end of the escape tunnel?